The Letters go to a forest

by Roger Knights

Near to the Lettermen's house there was a big dark forest.

forest

The Lettermen had always wondered what it was like in the forest, but had never dared to look inside.

scared

you first

One day, several Lettermen plucked up the courage to go into the forest.

No one wanted to be the first.

path

They followed a narrow path that led into the middle of the forest. At first, there were pretty flowers and lots of birds.

But the deeper into the forest they went, the darker it became. The Lettermen were beginning to feel a bit frightened.

dark

Soon it was so dark that
the Lettermen couldn't see
where they were going.
They kept bumping into
trees, bushes and
other Lettermen.

bump

house

Soon they thought they were completely lost. Then they came across a tiny little house, hidden in the darkest part of the wood.

yummy

When they got close to the house, they saw that it was made entirely out of sweets. The Lettermen couldn't believe their luck!

Not surprisingly, they began to eat. First the walls, then the window frames...

eat

With his mouth full of humbugs, one Letterman looked through a window.

look

He saw a wicked old witch stirring a huge cauldron of boiling water. She had a long nose and no teeth and was singing to herself in a high croaky voice.

witch

As she stirred her horrible mixture, she looked up and saw the Lettermen peering

in through the window. She smiled and beckoned to them.

boil

But the Lettermen thought they knew exactly what she wanted to boil in her cauldron. Them!

US

run

They ran as fast as their little legs would carry them, and hoped that the witch wouldn't chase after them.

They ran and ran until they were out of the forest and safe again. Now, when anyone asks the Lettermen if they would like to visit the forest, you can be sure of the answer...

safe